Bernard Young is a professional writer and performer who leads writing workshops for children and adults. He has given hundreds of performances in a variety of settings (from prisons to pubs, leisure centres to libraries, as well as colleges, schools, playgroups and supermarkets!). Bernard's poems have been broadcast on local and national radio, and feature in numerous anthologies of poetry for young readers.

Wanted Alive is Bernard's third collection of poetry for children, following on from *Double Talk* (written with Trevor Millum) and *Brilliant*!

Jessie Gillick studied illustration in York and Hull, and has been illustrating children's books ever since. This is her third book with Hands Up Books. She lives in Yorkshire with her three children and 2 cats.

British Library Cataloguing in Publication Data.
A catalogue record for this book is available from The British Library.

Published by Hands Up Books

ISBN 0-9542710-5-X

First published 2004
by
Hands Up Books,
4 Sandringham Cottages,
Brantingham
HU15 1QH
East Riding of Yorkshire

With special thanks to Michael Clark

Printed in England by Central Print Services, Hull

For information about all Hands Up Books publications, please contact:
Graham Denton (editor): handsup@handsup.karoo.co.uk

Reprinted 2010 by

York Publishing Services
64 Hallfield Road
Layerthorpe
York
YO31 7ZQ

www.yps-publishing.co.uk

WANTED ALIVE

Poems by Bernard Young

Bernard Young

Illustrations by Jessie Gillick

A Hands Up Books publication

CONTENTS

THE MR VISITOR TREPIDATION TRIOLET

I am Mr Visitor
and I'm in your school today.
I wonder what's in store
for Mr Visitor?
Will I be pleased I paid a visit or
be glad to get away?
I am Mr Visitor
and I'm in your school today.

TEACHER, WATCH OUT!

If I stare at you
You'll develop a twitch

If I ignore you
You'll start to itch

If I look through you
You'll not be heard

If I watch your lips
You'll muddle your words

If I close one eye
You'll feel unsure

If I close two
You'll disappear

So watch it!

If you set homework
I'll shut my eyes

And you'll be in
For a big surprise

You'll see!

CONFESSION TIME

'It's like 3 miles there
and 3 miles back
that walk to the front
in assembly
to collect a sticker
for being *Worker of the Week*.
I sometimes mess about
on a Thursday
to make sure I don't get it.'

'I'll tell you something,'
his teacher said, 'Sometimes,
when I'm out on a night
and there's a raffle,
I pray that my numbers
won't come up.
It's like 5 miles there
and 5 miles back
for me
if I have to claim a prize
in front of a roomful
of envious eyes.
I'd rather lose.'

THE MAGNIFICENT MALONE

It's our Mrs Jefferies up there.
I'd recognize her anwhere.
(Even under all that false facial hair).
It's our Mrs Jefferies up there.

She's up to her old tricks again.
Sawing ladies in half. (But causing no pain).
Pulling rabbits out of hats. (Just to entertain).
She's up to her old tricks again.

I'd heard she was once a magician.
She obviously doesn't want any recognition
now that she's part of the teaching profession.
I'd heard she was once a magician.

'Hey Mrs J your cover's blown.
When I get to school I'll let it be known
that Mrs Jefferies is *The Magnificent Malone*.
So Mrs J your cover's blown.'

But Mrs Jefferies shows no fear.
She commands me to be her volunteer.
Is she going to make me disappear?
(My parents will be livid once they hear).
But Mrs Jefferies shows no fear.

On stage she hisses in my ear,
'I'll make you suffer for the rest of the year
if this gets out. Is that clear?
(Then from nowhere ten white doves appear).
On stage she hisses in my ear.

Next day at school when our eyes meet
I look away, stare at my feet.
I know what will happen if I'm indiscreet
next day at school when our eyes meet.

EVERY NIGHT MR MILLER DREAMS

Every night Mr Miller dreams
of the day he will retire.
There'll be a small party
in the staff room
during the lunch hour
and at final assembly
he'll receive a major gift
from the whole school
plus presents
from individual pupils
who will be heartbroken
to see him leave.
Children, past and present
(some now grown up)
will file past to thank him
for being so inspirational
- for changing their lives.

In the evening
a large group of colleagues and friends
will take him out for drinks
and a meal.
There will be speeches
charting his impressive career
and praising his achievements.

He can't wait.

Day two. Week one. First job.
A long way to go.

Every night Mr Miller dreams.

THE SCHOOL FOR DAYDREAMERS

Lesson One

Gaze out
of the window.
Let your mind wander.
Do not listen to a word I say.
Begin...

I rang
a bell. I beat
a drum. No one stirred.
One heard. Your thoughts were far away.
Well done.

Homework

Drift off
during your tea.
Don't watch TV. Tune in
to the pictures inside your head.
Have fun.

THE OLD BOILER

Conditions here are arctic
We're sitting in our coats
Miss has got the sniffles
We've all got sore throats

We're wearing gloves or mittens
We cannot hold our pens
I'm sure you grt the picture
The boiler's failed again

Annually it happens
Every winter it's the same
The temperature's sub-zero
And the boiler is to blame

Thanks to the boiler
We all freeze
Thanks to the boiler
Our lessons cease

and we have to be sent home
at lunchtime.
What a shame!

Thanks to the boiler
Long may it rule
Thanks to the boiler
Our boiler's *really* cool!

THE GIGGLES

Our giggles are infectious.
They start off in our heads.
At first they're only rumours.
Then the rumours spread.

(Giggling is contagious.
It soon catches on.
But if you do it in the classroom
you find you're in the wrong.)

When asked about *The Giggles*
we won't know what to say
but we'll get into trouble
if they don't go away.

'Do tell me what's so funny,'
Miss Simpson will demand
but if we say, 'Nothing, Miss'
she won't understand.

She'll think we've got a secret
and I suppose we have
but we're completely baffled!
What was it made us laugh?

We need to find a reason.
She'll expect us to explain.
I just hope our explanation
doesn't set us off again.

Our giggles are infectious.
They start off in our heads.
At first they're only rumours.
Then the rumours spread...

(Note: Giggling *is* infectious.
Hard to resist. A tip:
it can be stifled
by biting your lower lip.)

HIS NAME IS ON THE BOARD AGAIN

His name is on the board again.
He doesn't care.
He's mad. Insane.

He should learn how to use his brain.
Or, better still, how to disappear.
His name is on the board again.

And it might as well remain.
It not being there is rare.
He's mad. Insane.

In the past he'd have got the cane.
Felt pain. But not (I'd guess) fear.
His name is on the board again.

There it is, in felt-tip, *Wayne*.
Another word for troublemaker.
He's mad. Insane.

And always to blame.
Get him out of here.
His name is on the board again.
He's mad. Insane.

BOSS OV SKEWLS

If I woz Boss ov Skewls
I wudent chaynj the rewls
but I wud ban speling tessts.

A WINTER'S TALE

Paul Perkins had annoyed me
since the term began
and yet I couldn't honestly say
he ever did anything wrong.
He *always* got his work done.
He *always* got it right.
I couldn't give him bad marks.
The lad was far too bright.
But he *always* had an answer.
He always looked so smug.
I felt that I should sort him out
yet I never could...

Until, one wintry weekend,
I saw him out alone.
I was walking my dog in the park.
He was heading home.
I hurled a snowball.
It got him in the neck.
I wanted to leap into the air
when he hit the icy deck.
But I appeared to appear from nowhere
asking, 'Are you alright Paul?
I do hope you haven't broken anything.
That looked like a nasty fall.'
I could tell he suspected something.
It was written on his face.
'I expect you slipped on the ice,' I said
He agreed that was the case.

That was many years ago.
Paul has long since gone.
He's probably forgotten all about it.
I never told anyone.
For I'm not proud of what I did.
What a way for a teacher to behave!
Did I *really* do such a thing?
Even I find it hard to believe.
But when I threw that snowball
it gave me such a thrill.
He never saw it coming.
The memory warms me still.

WANTED ALIVE: New Teacher for Cowboy School

Are you a sharpshooter
and quick on the draw?
Can you jangle your spurs
and lay down the law?

Yep!

If you enter a classroom
and the cowboys are rowdy
can you obtain silence
just by hollerin' 'Howdy!'?

Yep!

Are you as at home in the saddle
as you are holding chalk?
Do you like eating baked beans?
Can you drawl when you talk?

Yep!

Can you herd cattle
and control a lasso?
If you answer *Yep!*
this job could be for you.

Yep!

But you gotta look good
in a ten-gallon hat
if you want to work here.
Any problem with that?

Nope!

Then mosey on down
for a tough interview
and show the posse
what you can do.

But one piece of advice
I'll give to you, son,
if they start shootin'
you better run.

It'll mean they don't like you.
They don't want you around.
You ain't been successful
so get outa town!

DEAR GROWN-UPS

If kids got to rule the world
no doubt you'd expect the worst.
You'd prepare yourself for changes
and fearfully await the first.

You'd probably imagine
they'd demand chocolate every meal
and that the life of a grown-up
would become one long ordeal.

But *most* children I know
I am certain, I am sure,
would strive to save the planet
and put an end to war.

They'd work hard to ensure
no one was living in the street,
that all the animals were looked after
and everyone had enough to eat.

If kids got to rule the world
I think that you would find
that, just like *most* grown-ups,
they'd do what's best for mankind.

MOTHER! THINGS MUST CHANGE AROUND HERE

Untidy your bedroom.
It's looking far too neat.
And, unless you answer back,
I'll put you in the street.

Throw your coat down in the hall.
Don't hang it on a peg.
Burst open several bags of crisps
and devour them like a pig.

I hope you're not intending
to wash behind your ears.
If I find your neck's not dirty
there will be some tears.

And at every opportunity
you must watch TV.
I shall be very annoyed
if you're not glued to the set like me.

As for cooking, cleaning, laundry
- those jobs are still to do.
So cooking, cleaning, laundry
- those chores belong to you.

And, last but not least,
the most important new rule -
I shall be staying at home.
You will be going to school.

BARKING

It wouldn't have been so awful,
it wouldn't have seemed so bad,
if the daft bloke in the spotlight
had been someone else's dad.

It wouldn't have been us embarrassed.
It wouldn't have been us who whinged.
Another family would have suffered.
Other relatives would have cringed.

But it was our Dad up there.
It was our dad *having a go*.
It was our dad being laughed at.
Our Dad was part of the show.

He said he wouldn't go under.
He claimed he could stay in control.
He would resist the hypnotist.
His willpower we would extol.

But in no time Dad was barking
and crawling around on all fours.
He willingly begged for a biscuit
and whined to be let out of doors.

It really was a nightmare.
Not nice for his next of kin.
But when Dad returned to his seat
he swore he couldn't remember a thing.

Not acting like a Jack Russell?
Not being forced to sit up and beg?
'Not even,' he said, with a twinkle,
'biting that hypnotist's leg!'

THE WIZARD'S DOG

The wizard's dog
doesn't bury bones.
He hides stars.

He doesn't go walkies.
He flies.

He doesn't fetch sticks.
He brings back wands.

But he does chase
the witch's cat.

And when his master gets home
he goes crazy
with excitement and love.

So, in many ways,
he is a fairly ordinary
sort of dog.

The wizard's dog.

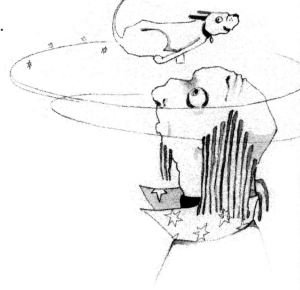

BEING A BEAR

He had his stamp and growl
He revealed just how he felt
You knew that he was grizzly
Before his rage you knelt

He bared his teeth and showed his claws
The sight you saw was grim
You got the message loud and clear
Stay away from him

But anger has departed
That Grizzly's upped and gone
He's become your Dad again
Nothing, now, is wrong

QUAKE

When dinosaurs have a falling out
When dinosaurs have a fight
Anyone with any sense
Keeps well out of sight

It's terrifying!

The ground trembles
The trees shake
Rocks rattle
Boulders break

It's like an earthquake!

When dinosaurs become friends again
Shake bony hands
Throw a party
Have a dance

It's terrifying!

Rocks rattle
Boulders break
The ground trembles
The trees shake

But those with any sense don't go
shouting:
'Be quiet, for goodness sake!'
They lie low
and quake.

THE HERO OF THE DAY

A one-eyed dalmation
is currently in custody
at the local police station.
If he belongs to you
or if you have any information
regarding his owners,
their home, its location,
then do get in touch.
You can be certain the whole nation
will applaud your part
in this overt operation
to transfer the aforementioned
and (it has to be said) *doleful* dalmation
to his rightful owners.

On his return their mood
will surely switch from sorrow to elation
and they may wish
to show their appreciation
by offering a reward
i.e. financial remuneration
i.e. money
to the hero of the day
i.e. You

The Hero of the Day!
But first you must earn that reputation.

MARY HAD A LITTLE MONSTER

Mary had a little monster
(his skin was green and yellow)
and everywhere that Mary went
that monster liked to follow.

He followed her to the supermarket
and helped himself to cheese. He
swallowed a bottle of cooking oil.
Ugh! He felt queasy.

He tottered past the cornflakes
and fell headfirst in the freezer,
landing with a bump
where the fish fingers and the peas are.

The supermarket manager was sent for.
He looked grim.
'Who owns this monster?' he bellowed.
'Who's responsible for him?'

'I am, sir,' said Mary
as sweetly as she could.
'I'm sorry he's been naughty.
He's usually very good.'

'I'll take him home and scold him, sir.
A telling off, I know, is due.
And I'll pay for any damage, sir,
if you want me to.'

'I suppose that won't be necessary,'
said the Manager (which was nice)
'but we'd better get that monster out
before he turns to ice.'

They dragged him from the freezer.
(He was a miserable blue).
They stood him in front of a heater
until he was sweating. *Phew*!

It was obvious his escapade
had given him a fright.
'All your own fault!' said Mary.
(But she hoped he was all right).

Mary still has a monster
and he's just as green and yellow
and *almost* everywhere that Mary goes
that monster likes to follow.

But supermarkets and monsters
clearly do not mix.
Monsters crash into cans of beans
and crush the Weetabix.

So, although Mary and her monster
continue to roam
when Mary shops for groceries
the monster stays at home.

TO THE GREAT PROVIDER

Dear Great Provider,
This is to thank you
for the delicious cheese
you so thoughtfully provide.
Thank you.

However,
(I do hope this doesn't seem ungrateful)
would it be possible to place it
by the side of our hole
and not on the spikes
of the thing that snaps
when we take a bite?
That would be most helpful.

It's just that,
as you may or may not know,
a member of my family
(my precious daughter, to be precise)
has not returned from dining out
and we fear her disappearance
has something to do
with the fierce snappy thing.
It doesn't like mice!

(This is not a criticism.
We would sooner pull out our own whiskers
than question your unquestionable wisdom.
We know you move in mysterious ways.)

Once again, Great Provider,
thank you for the wonderful cheese.
It's irresistible.

Yours humbly and appreciatively,

Montague Mouse

MESSAGE FROM A MISERABLE TORTOISE

To whom it may concern,

Don't expect
to see me today.

I'm fed up.
Depressed.
Withdrawn.

You can knock as hard as you like.
I'm not coming out.
Not even for a lettuce leaf.

I'm a hard nut to crack.
An unsociable bone.

Leave me alone.

SAD

Sorrowful
And
Dejected

Sombre
And
Depressed

So
Absolutely
Downcast

UNDER THE WEATHER

I hate being under the weather.
It's cold down here.
And damp.

I'd rather be over the moon
or head in the clouds.
Flying high.
Staring at stars.

Everything's getting on top of me.
I hate being under the weather.

SOMETHING TO LOOK FORWARD TO

Some day the sun will shine.
We'll step out and not get wet.
One day, but not just yet,
the weather will be fine.

That day will be yours and mine.
We'll sunbathe. Joyfully sweat.
Some day the sun will shine.
We'll step out and not get wet.

So don't grumble. Don't whine.
Don't lose hope. Don't fret.
Things will get better. You bet.

Look for an omen. A sign.
Some day the sun *will* shine.
We'll step out and not get wet.

ANOTHER VIEW

This place is full of scenery.
There's not a shop in sight.
You cannot buy a burger.
There's *nothing* here I like.

There's nothing here I like.
It's all hills and trees and lakes
and oldies who love hiking.
I *need* to phone my mates.

I need to phone my mates
and tell them what I'm going through;
how I have to trek for hours
just to admire a view.

'Just admire that view,'
is all my Dad can say.
It's driving me nuts.
I've *got* to get away.

I've got to get away
from fresh air and greenery.
I need noise and traffic.
This place is full of *scenery*!

TRAFFIC JAM

We started early
And travelled far
But now we're sick
Of being in the car

Traffic jam
Traffic jam
We're stuck in a traffic jam

When we set off
Six hours ago
We never imagined
We'd feel this low

Traffic jam
Traffic jam
We're stuck in a traffic jam

Mum is grumbling
Dad is growling
My brother's moaning
I feel like howling

Traffic jam
Traffic jam
We're stuck in a traffic jam

I fear I'll grow old
And my hair will be grey
By the time we begin
Our holiday

Traffic jam
Traffic jam
We're stuck in a traffic jam

This is unbearable
When will it end?
We may not be moving
But we're going round the bend

Traffic jam
Traffic jam
We're STILL STUCK in a TRAFFIC JAM!

IS DADDY TAKING US TO THE ZOO TOMORROW?

One little car
driving to the zoo.
Here comes another.
Now there are two.

Two travelling cars.
Happy as can be.
One overtakes them.
That makes three.

Three speeding cars.
Here's number four.
And in no time at all
here come some more
(and more and more and more and more
and more and more and more...)

One hundred cars.
Many in a hurry.
Five hundred cars.
At the front's a lorry.

It pulled out at a junction
and is moving oh so slow.
(Driving motorists to distraction -
that's not where they want to go!)

The journey stretching out ahead
has become a traffic jam.
But when did that happen?
How did it begin?

With that solitary car, of course,
heading to the zoo.
It was joined by others
full of folk like me and you.

But did it reach its destination?
It was going to the zoo, you said.
Oh yes, but when it arrived the gates were closed
and all the animals had gone to bed.

Is Daddy taking us to the zoo tomorrow?
NO WAY!

COACHES, CARS AND LORRIES

We'd really enjoy living here
(And so, we think, would you)
If coaches, cars and lorries
Passed by instead of through

We curse the constant traffic
The never ending flow
If only coaches, cars and lorries
Passed by instead of through

You should hear our windows rattle
You should witness how we sigh
When coaches, cars and lorries
Pass through instead of by

We dream that in the future
(And let's hope our dream comes true)
All the coaches, cars and lorries
Will pass by instead of through

BEST FRIENDS

Would a best friend
    Eat your last sweet
    Talk about you behind your back
    Have a party and not ask you

Mine did.

Would a best friend
    Borrow your bike without telling you
    Deliberately forget your birthday
    Avoid you whenever possible

Mine did.

Would a best friend
    Turn up on your bike
    Give you a whole packet of your favourite sweets
    Look you in the eye

Mine did.

Would a best friend say
    Sorry I talked about you behind your back
    Sorry I had a party and didn't invite you
    Sorry I deliberately forgot your birthday
    - I thought you'd fallen out with me

Mine did.

And would a best friend say, simply,
    Never mind
    That's OK

I did.

Hi

Wanna go
to a
parti
Jenni

Fizzi
pop
and plenti
ful music

Dance
and eat
It'll be
great

I
just
can't
wait

Hurri
up
Send a
repli

(If it's
no
I'll wanna know
Y?)

WHAT DO I KNOW?

Rather than say hello
my best friend's dad
always greets me with
'Now then, what do you know?'

I'm tempted to tell him...

1. *That the Ancient Greeks built
    the Parthenon*
2. *That eight eights are sixty-four*
3. *That Robert Louis Stevenson wrote Treasure Island*
4. *That Henry VIII's third wife was Jane Seymour*
5. *That the world's highest mountain is Mount Everest*
6. *That not wearing seatbelts is against the law*
7. *That Canberra is the capital of Australia*
8. *That the Three Wise Men were Caspar, Balthazar
    and Melchior*
9. *That spiders have eight legs*
10. *That the Tyrannosaurus Rex was the largest
    carnivorous dinosaur*

...but I don't.

I say what
he wants to hear,
my usual answer:
'Not a lot.'

ABOUT ME

I'm in Rome
I'm in Cromer

I'm in chrome
I'm not in aroma

I'm in time
I'm in slime!

I'm in meat
I'm in mime

I'm in measure
I'm in mellow

I'm in melon
I'm not in yellow

I must be famous
I'm in fame

Am I in trouble?
I'm in blame!

I'm in dome
I'm in gnome

Now you've met *me*
I'm going home

MEAN MILLY

Milly wasn't a cat lover.
She wasn't a fan.
She hated the sight of them.
If they saw her they ran.

Because little Milly Marwood was mean to cats.

* * *

Coming home from school one day
she saw a ginger tom on a garden wall.
Before she could push him off
he stuck his face into hers.
(They were eyeball to eyeball.
She could smell his fishy breath).
He spoke:

'Mean to cats.
Mean to cats.
We've had enough of Milly
being mean to cats.'

'What!' gasped Milly.

'Mean to cats,'
hissed a voice from behind.
'Mean to cats.
We've had enough of Milly
being mean to cats.'

She turned.

A furry army faced her.

'Mean to cats,' they sang.
'Mean to cats.
It's time little Milly
stopped being mean to cats.'

She felt teeth in her ankle.
The tom clawed her cheek.
That terrible girl, suddenly,
was defenceless and weak.

So there wasn't a struggle,
there wasn't a sound,
when mean Milly Marwood
was dragged to the ground...

* * *

Cats curled up on knees
that evening
as if nothing had happened.

They stretched in front of fires,
washed themselves,
licked their full stomachs.

In kitchens
bowls of cat food remained untouched.

At home
Milly's meal congealed.

'Where can that girl have got to?'
muttered her mother.

She opened the front door wide
and called into the night:

'Milly! Where are you Milly?
Here Milly, Milly.
Here Milly, Milly...'

A WITCH MUST HAVE A CAT

A witch must have a cat

So I cast a spell
But got a rat
I mixed a potion
Out flew a bat

I wasn't very happy about that
A witch must have a cat

I went to the pet shop
They locked me out
They said, 'You're the sort of customer
we can do without.'

I wasn't very happy about that
A witch must have a cat

So I'm knocking on doors
Ratatat-tat
I'm looking for
A suitable cat

If you're the owner
I'll pay well
But there'll be trouble
If you won't sell

I won't be very happy about that
A witch must have a cat

Yes I'm knocking on doors
Ratatat-tat
I'll be knocking on yours
Ratatat-tat

Ratatat-tat
Ratatat-tat
A witch *must* have a cat

A WITCH'S CAT SHOULD GIVE YOU A FRIGHT

I have a ginger kitten
and everyone I meet
says, 'What a lovely little cat.
Your kitten is so sweet.'

But I need...

A cat who will scratch.
A cat who will spit.
A black cat who'll match
my witch's outfit.

A cat who is cute
cannot be right.
A witch's cat
should give you a fright.

When I'm not being a witch
my cat is just fine.
She plays and she purrs
and I'm glad she is mine.

But when I'm out with the broom,
dressed in the hat,
to complete the costume
I need a mean cat.

A cat who will hiss.
A cat full of spite.
A cat as black
as a moonless night.

A cat who is cute
cannot be right.
A witch's cat
should give you a fright.

A WIZARD IN A BLIZZARD

A wizard in a blizzard
gasped, 'This will not do.
My beard is frozen solid.
My toes have all turned blue.
I need to use my powers
to calm this raging storm.
The temperature's sub-zero.
I prefer it warm.'

A wizard in a blizzard
decided that he would
recreate the summer
as quickly as he could.
With a wave of his wand
and one slowly whispered word
     s-u-n-s-h-i-n-e
an amazing transformation occurred.

All the snowmen vanished.
The solid lake was thawed
and the remarkable change in temperature
just could not be ignored.
Suddenly it was tropical.
The wizard thought, 'How nice.
This is so much pleasanter
than that nasty snow and ice.'

But all the skiers and the snowboarders
and the owners of swift sleighs
and the disappointed snowballers
and those who loved to skate
came looking for the wizard
and their eyes were filled with hate.
'They do look,' he said to himself,
'as if they're in a bit of a state.'

'They could do with a holiday,
a little time to calm down,
and I need a break
before I leave town.'
So he turned some into sandcastles
and some into boats
and some into donkeys
and some into fishermen's floats.

'When I've had enough sun
and I'm ready to go
they'll become as they were
and be back in the snow.
But never again,
without a good reason,
will I mess with the weather
or alter the season.'

THE WIZARD'S QUEST

I appear as if from nowhere.
I jump out from behind the sofa.

I am attired in a shimmering robe.
I'm wearing Mum's old dressing gown.
(The one with holes in).

I am on a dangerous quest.
I'm hungry.

I aim my wand at the fierce red-eyed snarling fire-breathing creature guarding the entrance to the cave.
I point my pencil at our kitten sitting in front of the kitchen cupboard.

I command the mad beast to leave or face death.
I say 'Shift!' and gently push her with my foot.

He sensibly accepts defeat and departs.
She hisses but moves.

I enter the cave victoriously.
I open the cupboard.

At last the ancient treasure is mine.
I take the chocolate biscuits to my bedroom.

Success!
Success!

DAYS LIKE THAT

Bowled out as soon as you go into bat
All of us have days like that
It's a big disappointment
A cause for regret
All of us have days like that

You try to be funny but your jokes just fall flat
All of us have days like that
It's a kick in the teeth
Something you'd choose to forget
All of us have days like that

You hear yourself being described as a rat
All of us have days like that
It's a moment of pain
You feel you've been struck
All of us have days like that

You'd such high hopes when you went into bat
All of us have days like that
But it all went wrong
And you were out for a duck
All of us have days like that

But sometimes you're the world's best acrobat
All of us have days like that
When you can ignore the harness
And decline the net
All of us, thank goodness, have days like that

MOANING MINNIE

'You could moan for England,'
is what Mum said to me.
When asked for his opinion
Dad said, 'I agree.'

He entered me in a regional heat
and I easily got through,
but by the time I reached the final
I said 'Uh! Do I have to?'

They pushed me onto the platform
and gave me a microphone
so I took a breath as deep as the sea
and then began to moan.

I moaned about the weather.
I moaned about TV.
I moaned about my brother.
I moaned about being me.

I moaned about the whole wide world.
I moaned about our sofa.
I planned to moan for hours
but they said, 'STOP! It's over.'

'That's it. You're the winner.
Now what have you got to say?'
'Me? A winner! Wow!
You've really made my day.'

'Sorry,' they said, 'Trick question.
A ruse. A crafty test.
You would have kept on moaning
if you really were the best.'

I could have moaned. But didn't.
I suddenly didn't care.
It was Mum and Dad who went on and on
about it being unfair.

I don't want to moan for England.
At last my goal's worthwhile.
I'll strive to be the owner
of the nation's widest smile.

LADY LOLLIPOP

Lollipop Lady
Lady Lollipop
She's got the power
To make the traffic stop

When she steps out
With her lollipop sign
The people on the pavement
Sure feel fine

They know they can go
They'll be OK
"Thank you very much"
Is what they all should say

To the lollipop lady
Lady Lollipop
She's got the power
To make the traffic stop

She's there for me
She's there for you
Standing in the rain
Doing what she's got to do

She makes it safe
For us to cross
Halts all the traffic
Shows who's boss

It's the lollipop lady
Lady Lollipop
She's got the power
To make the traffic stop

She's the lollipop lady
Lady Lollipop
And she's got the power
She's got the power
She's got the power
To make the traffic......STOP!

CHECK IT OUT

If you've got a bike
        Check it out
Before you ride
        Check it out

Do your brakes work?
Are your tyres O.K.?
Is your seat wobbly?
Will you be safe today?

        Check it out
        Check it out

Do your lights shine?
Are your reflectors clean?
Can you see where you're going?
Can *you* be seen?

        Check it out
        Check it out

Are your hands on the handlebars?
Are you in the right gear?
Do you know how to signal?
Is your helmet secure?

        Check it out
        Check it out

To make sure your bike
Is as good as new
Now you know
What you should do

Check it out
No fussing
Check it out
No messing
Check it out
And you'll be laughing

Check it out
Check it out
Check it out out out

BE A BRAINY BIKER

Your brain is brilliant
Keep it safe and sound
Encase it in a helmet
In case it hits the ground

Your life is precious
Don't throw it away
Stick a helmet on your head
If you bike today

BIKER

Bike on the left
Look to the right
Watch for cars
Keep 'em in sight

Look down the road
Glance down the lane
That wicked motor
Is coming again

Look over your shoulder
Stretch out your arm
Take some care
You'll come to no harm

Move to the middle
Slide to the right
This ain't line dancing
But you're doing alright

Here come the children
Heading to school
Observe the crossing
And the highway rule
Stop when you're told to
Don't be a fool
Cos' that lollipop lady
She really cool

Bike on the left
Look to the right
Watch for cars
Keep 'em in sight

Don't ride on the pavement
Don't clutter the gutter
Glide so smooth
Don't ride like a stutter
Enjoy yourself
But you better
Take care round the idiot
Beware of the nutter

Bike on the left
Look to the right
Watch for cars
Keep 'em in sight

Look down the road
Glance down the lane
That wicked motor
Is coming...coming...coming...again!

Bernard Young & Trevor Millum

JUST HAVING A LAUGH

He thought that it was fun
to play kerby on the road.
He thought that it was great
to kick a football in the street.
He thought it was a laugh
to play chicken with his mates
and it was...for a while.

He thought it was fantastic
when he bunny-hopped on highways
and skateboarded on the pavement
and roller bladed round the cars.
He thought it was a laugh
to take chances with his life
and it was...for a while.

He thought that it was fun
and that nothing could go wrong
until a speeding van
met this little man head-on
and threw him in the air.
You should have seen him soar!
He took off from here
and then lay crumpled..........over there.

He was rushed to hospital
and hastily operated on.
For a while it looked as though
he might pull through
and live. And, being young and strong,
he did.....for a night.....and a day,
then passed away.

His mum and dad aren't laughing.
It's not a laughing matter.
His sister isn't laughing.
Nor his friends in school.
His grandparents aren't laughing.
They feel they'll never laugh again.

Who'd have thought
just having a laugh
would cause a lifetime's pain?

HEAD CASE

I steered clear
of protective headgear
when I rode my bike.
I didn't want my friends
to stare
or laugh or jeer
or call me a wimp
or a geek
or any of those other insults
I used to fear.

So, no hemet for me.

I cycled
with my head uncovered.
Which is why I've ended up here.

Still, I've almost recovered.

And hospital food's not bad.
And the nurses are nice.
But the doctors are keeping an eye
on my head.
Monitoring my brain.
They need to make sure I'm really O.K.

I'm hoping I'll go home soon.

I still won't wear a helmet.
Not because I look daft
or care about what people say.
They can say what they like.

It's just that I don't fancy
ever getting back
on a bike.

THE TAPE MEASURE KID

She's The Tape Measure Kid
She's never nonplussed
She's The Tape Measure Kid
She's got everything sussed

No crime is too big
No crime is too small
The Tape Measure Kid
Tackles them all

She swings into action
At just the right height
Any corner she gets into
Is never too tight

She enters through windows
She squeezes through cracks
She surprises the villains
With measured attacks

She uses her tape
Like a cowboy's lasso
To bring down the baddies
So the town's safe for you

If there was a contest
She'd win the cup
As a crime fighter
She sure measures up

She's The Tape Measure Kid
She's got everything sussed
She's The Tape Measure Kid
She's never nonplussed

LESLEY PRESLEY

Grab some earplugs
Get your coat
Lesley Presley is opening her throat

Yeah, Lesley Presley is letting rip
Swivelling her hips
Curling her lip

Note after note
Coming out wrong
Lesley Presley is destroying a song

Our Aunt Lesley
A kindly soul
But not quite the Queen of Rock 'n' Roll!

MY TEENAGE BROTHER IS FROM ANOTHER PLANET

He moons around.
He stares into space.
Red spots erupt
all over his face.

He still likes football
but dreams about girls.
He now inhabits
an alien world.

That's it! He's an alien!
It's official. It's true.
He's been taken over.
But what can I do?

It's too late to save him
so the plan must be
to prevent the same thing
happening to me.

NICK (THE NAUGHTY NICKER)

When Nick went out nicking
he was caught
in the nick of time
and is now spending time
in the nick.

In his time
he's nicked knick-knacks,
a pickaxe,
a pick-up,
a picture
and a picnic.

He's bad news.

If you need to choose
a new friend don't pick Nick.

(* He even nicked his nickname!)

THE BRITISH BOBBY

We are British policemen
Bobbies on the beat
Victorian crime-stoppers
Patrolling London's streets

Our eyes are peeled for pickpockets
There are lots of them about
We give chase and blow our whistles
And get our truncheons out

Sir Robert Peel created us
That's why some call us peelers
Our job is to protect you
From murderers and stealers

We are British policemen
Bobbies on the beat
We've got brand new helmets
And great big bloomin' feet

CHRISTMAS EVE

It's getting dark and starting to rain
when Rabbit catches the evening train.

Clutching a brown paper bag (full of carrots)
he hops aboard
and is relieved to find an empty carriage.

He's been visiting a small market town.
Quite a long day for him.
He's pleased to sit down.

Steam drifts past his window.
He falls asleep.
It will take a lot to wake him now.

A guard (or is he a policeman?)
enters the carriage, picks Rabbit up
and places him (with his carrots)
in the luggage rack.

Other passengers pile in. They're all wearing
thick coats. Some have umbrellas.
Men in bowler hats. Women in bonnets.
Shawls.

'Just in time,' says one red-faced gentleman.

They settle into their seats. Bags, bonnets,
not coats, are disposed of in the luggage rack.
A pipe is lit. A cigar.

The journey begins.

Rabbit stirs.

'I love Christmas,' says a voice.

'Indeed,' says another.

'Merry Christmas and God Save the Queen,'
says a third.

'How nice this is,' thinks Rabbit,
as the train burrows into the tunnel.
'The dark. The train. The rain.

All is well.'

He sleeps and smells carrots.

CHRISTMAS: A Celebration

I love the tinsel
I love the tree
I love the cards
And the roast turkey

I love the crackers
I love the pud
I love the chocs
That taste so good

I love hearing carols
How my heart lifts
I love sending presents
And receiving gifts

I love the parties
And the pantomime
I'm just mad
About Christmas time

I see relatives
I visit friends
And I'm always sad
When Christmas ends...

But then I start looking forward to next year

A DOOR BANGING

A door banging
A banging door
An ill wind blowing?
Who goes there?

Has good luck
Just slipped in?
Is misfortune
Leaving?

A door banging
A banging door
Good or bad?
I can't be sure

Take no chances
Shut it, quick
Turn the key
Let me hear the click

A door banging
A banging door
I can't help but wonder
What's in store?

ACKNOWLEDGMENTS

The author's poems were first published as indicated:

About Me, *The Trying Flapeze*, OUP 2004

Being a Bear, *A Bag of Stars*, Hands Up Books 2002

Best Friends, *Poems About You and Me*, Wayland 1998

Every Night Mr Miller Dreams, *The Teacher's Revenge*, Macmillan 2003

Lesley Presley, *Turn that Racket Down!*, Red Fox 2001

Message From a Miserable Tortoise, *Taking My Human For a Walk*, Macmillan 2003

Mother! Things Must Change Around Here, *The Prime Minister is 10 Today*, Macmillan 2003

My Teenage Brother is From Another Planet, *Aliens Stole My Underpants 2*, Macmillan 2001

Nick (The Naughty Nicker), *I Say, I Say, I Say*, OUP 2003

Quake, *Dangerous Dinosaurs*, Macmillan 2002

Teacher, Watch Out!, *Ye New Spell Book*, Macmillan 2002

The British Bobby, *Hysterical Historical Poems - The Victorians*, Macmillan 2000

The Old Boiler, *Who Rules the School Now?*,
Macmillan 2003

The School for Daydreamers, *Spectacular Schools*,
Macmillan 2004

To the Great Provider, *Loony Letters & Daft Diares*,
Macmillan 2003

Under the Weather, *Don't Get Your Knickers in a Twist*,
Macmillan 2002

Wanted Alive: New Teacher for Cowboy School,
Spectacular Schools, Macmillan 2004

The Giggles, *When the Teacher Isn't Looking...*,
Macmillan 2001